A CHOICE OF
THOMAS HARDY'S POEMS

A CHOICE OF
THOMAS HARDY'S POEMS

Made by
GEOFFREY GRIGSON

Illustrated by
Glynn Thomas

MACMILLAN

Introduction © Geoffrey Grigson 1969
Illustrations © Macmillan and Co Ltd 1969

First published 1969 *by*
MACMILLAN AND CO LTD
Little Essex Street London WC2
and also at Bombay Calcutta and Madras
Macmillan South Africa (*Publishers*) *Pty Ltd Johannesburg*
The Macmillan Company of Australia Pty Ltd Melbourne
The Macmillan Company of Canada Ltd Toronto
Gill and Macmillan Ltd Dublin

Printed in Great Britain by
WESTERN PRINTING SERVICES LTD
Bristol

CONTENTS

A CHOICE OF
THOMAS HARDY'S POEMS

THOMAS HARDY

Poets are often secretive. A poet I knew – yet did not really know – surprised me by saying how much he liked to talk about his inside concerns. It was hard to talk with him at all, or to make him talk. He was usually silent, he walked around with the face of a dark secret.

I think he meant that he would have liked to talk about himself, if he could have found some way of being less aloof, and if he could have found someone who would have been ready to listen.

In fact he never talked about himself except in his poems, and then in an autobiography which was not published until after his death.

Thomas Hardy was rather the same. He became one of the most famous writers in Europe (not for his poems, which he preferred, but for his novels), yet in day to day life he remained inward and enigmatic. In his poems – many of them were unpublished for years – he told secrets of his feelings and conclusions about being born, and existing and dying; about loving and being loved or not loved; about hurting and being hurt, about misery and being happy, being young, and being old; about God – and whether a God existed; and if a God did exist, whether he realised what he had been up to when he invented man?

Then Hardy realized we should want to know something about himself, about the actual writer who had lived and worked so long in Dorset. So he went through his notebooks and diaries. Everything that seemed to the point in explaining Thomas Hardy or Thomas Hardy's writing he put on one side; everything that seemed to him just his own business, not ours, he destroyed.

From the material which seemed to matter, he arranged memoirs of himself; these were to be published after his death, as if entirely by another hand. Then he died in his ugly house at Max Gate outside Dorchester, having settled his account with life and with that flow of time which none of us can resist.

The account had been settled in his poems. He had written so much around things we know, wind, rain, Roman roads, love, churchyards, summer-houses gone shaky, garden seats which have lost their colour, that when he died, on January 11th, 1928 – an old, old man of 87 – it was as if a part of our own lives had been smudged out.

I remember his death. At the time I was in my twenties, working in a newspaper office in London; but Hardy and his poems seemed modern, in spite of his age; and when the words THOMAS HARDY DEAD jerked out of one of the news machines which feed events endlessly into newspaper offices, it was as if damage had been done to life. When the work of that night was over, I walked home between 'the files of formal houses' (that was Hardy's way of saying, in one poem, how little he cared for towns or cities), experiencing a first grief of the kind which is both public and personal.

When I reached home after midnight, I did what many people must have done at the first knowledge of this old poet's death. I read to myself the poem *Afterwards* (which is to be found on page 91, the last poem but one in this selection).

In this poem Hardy had written about his own death and so about everybody's death; he had defined being dead and being alive by mentioning, one after another, things we enjoy, things the dead have enjoyed: the new delicacies in early summer, the soundless flying of nightjars, the way one meets with surprise a hedgehog on the lawn at midnight, and hopes that the hedgehog will not be killed or interfered with; a black sky full of bright constellations; the intermittent tolling of a bell:

> *And will any say when my bell of quittance is heard in the gloom,*
> *And a crossing breeze cuts a pause in its outrollings,*
> *Till they rise again, as they were a new bell's boom,*
> *'He hears it not now, but used to notice such things'?*

Hardy's life was over, but as I read that poem on this night of his death, he seemed – as he still seems – alive. He had left himself behind, he had left himself alive and active, in our language, in his use of it, in his poems; which is what happens inevitably – and happily – when a good poet has laid his finger on the warmth and coldness of life.

But let us go back to Hardy's beginnings.

'Far away', again, 'from the files of formal houses', he was the son of small builder who lived at Stinsford in Dorset, where Hardy was born in 1840. At first he was rather a weak child, who grew up both sociable and aloof, both friendly and secretive, never, for example, liking to be touched by someone else's hand.

His home was a thatched house between heath and woodland, up a lane, not easy to find. Here, in Bockhampton hamlet, his father had a field, and some sand-pits useful for his business. Hardy wrote that his father hadn't the soul or the ambition of a tradesman (though he was successful in his trade): one thing he liked was going up on the heath, by himself, in the hot weather, then 'lying on a bank of thyme or camomile with the grasshoppers leaping over him'. When Hardy remembered and recorded that, I think he had himself in mind, as well as his father. They were like one another in many respects.

Hardy kept one very bright recollection about his home, that when the sun moved round towards evening, its light came through a window on to the wall of the staircase which his father had painted Venetian red. For about a quarter of an hour the direct light intensified the colour. As he watched it growing deeper, the small Hardy would say to himself, from a hymn he knew, 'And now another day is gone.' Many of his poems were to be about the passing of time, and the change from light to darkness, from life to death.

Another thing he remembered about his 'world of shepherds and plough-men', just outside the town world of Dorchester, the capital of Dorset, was that nightingales sang within three feet of the bedroom windows. Very nice. But he never became the kind of poet to write about nightingales, or to write about nature for itself. He said that nature had no mind, he said that natural things, much as he noticed them, were unimportant compared to human things, compared, for instance, to the hollow worn in the doorstep of a house by men's feet, going in and out, generation after generation.

The first poem Hardy wrote was about his home and its situation, but also about the way they had changed:

> Behind, the scene is wilder. Heath and furze
> Are everything that seems to grow and thrive
> Upon the uneven ground. A stunted thorn
> Stands here and there, indeed; and from a pit

(which would have been one of his father's sand-pits)

> An oak uprises, springing from a seed
> Dropped by some bird a hundred years ago.

> *In days bygone –*
> *Long gone – my father's mother, who is now*
> *Blest with the blest, would take me out to walk.*
> *At such a time I once inquired of her*
> *How looked the spot when first she settled here.*
> *The answer I remember. 'Fifty years*
> *Have passed since then, my child, and change has marked*
> *The face of all things. Yonder garden-plots*
> *And orchards were uncultivated slopes*
> *O'ergrown with bramble bushes, furze and thorn :*
> *That road a narrow path shut in by ferns,*
> *Which, almost trees, obscured the passer-by.*
>
> *'Our house stood quite alone, and those tall firs*
> *And beeches were not planted. Snakes and efts*
> *Swarmed in the summer days, and nightly bats*
> *Would fly about our bedrooms. Heathcroppers[1]*
> *Lived on the hills, and were our only friends;*
> *So wild it was when first we settled here.'*

When Hardy lived in this isolated house more than a hundred years ago, the country was often a cruel environment – crueller for land labourers than it had been at any time in English history. Wages were only a few shillings a week, the poor were made to feel shame at being poor, and were treated with a condescension, a condescending charity, or indifference, which was hard to put up with. Poverty led to crime, people were still hanged – and hanged in public.

When Hardy was 13 or 14 he had seen a woman hanged in Dorchester. When Hardy was 16, a man was to be hanged at Dorchester Prison at eight o'clock on a summer morning. Hardy climbed on to the heath at the back of the house and focussed his father's telescope on the prison and the gallows, nearly three miles away, just when the hanging took place. The murderer was dressed in white fustian. 'At the moment of his placing the glass to his eye the white figure dropped downwards, and the faint note of the town clock struck eight. . . . He seemed alone on the heath with the hanged man, and crept homeward wishing he had not been so curious.'

[1] Shaggy heathland ponies.

The Hardy family were reasonably well off, even if his father hadn't the tradesman's soul. They saw much of the pleasanter side of living in the country, father and son, for instance, going round to play the violin (for pleasure and neighbourliness, not for money) at marriages and parties. But Hardy never forgot the degradation of the poor and the effects of poverty, hopelessness and oppression on the way men live, and the way they die at last.

Yet as a poet and as a novelist he was to write of all men who are shut up in what he thought the cage of existence, not only of the ones so miserably paid ten shillings a week for long hours of the heaviest labour.

Hardy had to earn. So improving on his father's trade as a builder, he became an architect. His father built houses and repaired them, and restored churches: his son would design houses and plan restorations, becoming a respectable businessman. So he began – though the prospect left him uneasy – by drawing for architects in Dorchester and Weymouth, and in London, thinking on and off that he would rather be a poet, or a writer at any rate about the emotions which filled him.

He wrote poems, in between his architectural work. He sent them to editors. Editors, who thought them rugged and ragged, sent them back again. They were unlike poems by Keats, or Tennyson, or Rossetti, they were unlike the current idea of what poems should be. This failure with editors made Hardy think of writing novels, which might sell, and prove a more reliable way to independence.

For his first novel, which seemed too socialistic, too much against the moneyed class and the way those with money were insolent to those without money, he could not find a publisher. He was luckier with his second novel, *Desperate Remedies*, which was published in 1871. It was a beginning, if it did not earn him very much. Hardy was soon able to give up drawing and working for architects. He went on writing novels for a quarter of a century. All that while it was poems he would sooner have written. The novels – *Far from the Madding Crowd, The Return of the Native, The Mayor of Casterbridge, Tess of the D'Urbervilles, Jude the Obscure* – made him famous, and free, but in writing them he came to think he had done no more than exchange one trade for another.

Yet he did not altogether abandon poetry: he was a poet, he would have feelings about our existence, that most involved of puzzles, something would happen to him, he would see a comet, he would see a name on a gravestone, a face exquisitely appealing, a dwarf leading a giant at a circus, a boy on a station platform playing his violin to a convict in handcuffs, and words would well up inside him like a sudden spring out of the ground, he would shape and complete the words into stanzas or a sonnet or a story poem. Then – since editors had to be satisfied with another and another instalment of a serialized novel, since money had to be earned – he would put the poems away in a drawer.

They did not come out of the drawer until Hardy was nearly sixty, in 1898. Now, his tiresome trade given up, his novels done with, but continuing to earn him a livelihood, he had leisure to prepare and publish his first book of verse, including in it things he had written so long before, as a young architect of twenty-five or twenty-six.

It was the trade of novelist, all the same, which had enabled him to marry; and it was his young love affair with Emma Lavinia Gifford, a girl he had met on the cliffs of north Cornwall in 1870, when he was nearly 30 years old, which mattered most to Hardy in his life. It was this girl, and the woman she became, who caused him to write his strongest, tenderest, saddest poems; it was this girl – had all gone well with the two of them – who might almost have reconciled Hardy to existence.

Hardy and Emma Gifford met on a dry, windy March night after he had spent the day travelling from his parents' home in Stinsford. He was to report on the restoration of St Juliot church, and when he rang the door-bell at the rectory, he was received, not by the rector, who was ill in bed, not by the rector's wife who was upstairs looking after him, but by the rector's sister-in-law.

He saw by lamplight a girl in brown, who seemed very 'living', and graceful, who had a perfect complexion, below a coiled abundance of corn-coloured hair.

Rather embarrassed by having to receive him, she was not quite so impressed in his favour as he was in hers: his accent wasn't quite right, she thought him older than his 29 years, marked his beard, his rather shabby overcoat and his 'business appearance', though afterwards, she wrote, 'he seemed younger and by daylight especially so'. She was also surprised to discover that a blue paper in the pocket of his shabby overcoat hadn't been a plan of the church but the manuscript of a poem.

After dinner the girl and her sister sang duets.

Next day Hardy made a note, in a joining of sadness to happiness which

14

was just like him, about a funeral in St Juliot and a man tolling the bell, dismantled and upside down, by lifting the clapper and letting it fall against the side.

On the fourth day he left at dawn, after a candlelit breakfast.

The girl was agitated. Sometime after, Hardy seems to have written *At the Word 'Farewell'* (page 42), which describes how he stepped out to her on the grey lawn before saying his farewell:

> *Even then the scale might have been turned*
> *Against love by a feather –*
> *But crimson one cheek of hers burned*
> *When we came in together.*

Certainly in the days after he reached home he wrote *When I Set Out for Lyonnesse* (page 39 – Lyonnesse being Cornwall), about having magic in his eyes on his return, and a radiance around him which people noticed – including perhaps Hardy's architect employer, to whom he presented his account for £6. 10. 9.

Four years later, when he felt he could earn enough money by writing, Thomas Hardy and Emma Gifford were married.

Thirty-eight years later Emma Gifford – Emma Hardy – died, after years upon years in which there had been much coldness between them, and in which she had come to think, in their quite comfortless house (as someone who had visited the Hardys in their old age, described it to me), that she had married a man who was inferior to herself by the standards of class, a man whose poems and opinions were no more important than her own.

Thomas Hardy, full of remorse for his share of the division between them, wrote new love poems about her. He wrote *The Voice* (page 76) a month after her funeral, remembering the air-blue gown she had worn in the first summer of their acquaintanceship in Cornwall, when she would wait for him by the 'church-town', the church-place, of St Juliot.

Then in the first March after she died, old Hardy, himself 72 years old, travelled down to St Juliot again, where they had met on the dry, windy night in March forty-three years before; and wrote more poems of love and regret, poems in which he recalled and re-lived their first happiness together on the Cornish cliffs.

When you read these poems, *After a Journey* (page 77), *The Phantom Horsewoman* (page 79), *Where the Picnic Was* (page 82), and *A Man was*

Drawing Near to Me (page 40), remember that not all love poems are written by poets when they are young. And remember, about these poems in particular, something Hardy believed – that a poet's real aim (he was quoting from a friend) 'should be to touch our hearts by showing his own'.

After his wife's death, he did marry again, for comfort and convenience, but it was Emma –

> *I should have kissed her if the rain*
> *Had lasted a minute more*

who had been his radiance.

Hardy meant his poems to tell us about the feelings excited in him by human life. For several deliberate reasons he did not make his poems smooth and even, they are not all of identical shape, with lines of identical length, they are not full of expected 'poetry' words, the rhymes are not always exact, and the rhythms are not always regular.

Hardy knew the way we are pleased by slight irregularities in poems, as in the pattern of arches, windows and so on, which he studied in his restoration of ancient parish churches. And he said that he wanted, like medieval painters, not to present things in his poetry exactly as they are, but to distort them, to make this or that feature in them larger, smaller, narrower, to alter their proportions, so as to make us see the particular features, the particular meanings we mightn't otherwise have noticed.

Hardy called art – the arts of writing, of building, of making pictures – 'a disproportioning of realities'. His own art was 'to intensify the expression of things'.

When Hardy wrote, people were not always prepared for that. Often they were upset if poems failed to be sweet and pretty. Reviewers told him he was too gloomy. Hardy replied gently he was asking questions about life. When he was old, editors still occasionally found poems by Hardy too much for them. The poem he liked best (poets often dislike their poems once they are written and flown) was *A Trampwoman's Tragedy*, refused by an editor, in 1902, because it was a poem 'he could not possibly print in a family periodical'. Read it and see (page 34).

About Hardy's activity as a poet you may also like to know that although he wrote his first poem – the one I have mentioned about his home – when he was between 17 and 20, he only began writing poetry in earnest when he was 25 (for another five years after that he was not sure what he was going to do in life). He continued writing poems, on and off, till he died, old, weak and shrivelled. A poem which is surely most moving and strong, about the end of the First World War (page 46), he did not write until he was 80. He was working on poems in his last weeks when he was 87.

Sometimes the seed of a poem would lie in him for years before it was encouraged, or permitted, to grow. When he was in Cornwall in 1870 he watched an old horse drawing a harrow. The memory of this came back to him forty-five years later (perhaps he had jotted it down in a notebook) and caused him to write *In Time of 'The Breaking of Nations'* (page 33), again when nations were fighting in the First World War.

Don't think of Hardy, although some superior people have written of him in that way, as an old simpleton from the country (as if towns did not also breed their simpletons). He was much at home in London, he liked travelling across the Channel, he liked pictures and art galleries, he liked great cathedrals. But he also needed to go back to familiar silence and loneliness.

There Hardy would notice other things, such as ruins, wind-marks on water, prehistoric burial mounds, roses ripped from a wall, because they all spoke of the way we grow old and die and are forgotten. Also glow-worms, water-lilies, water-mills or mill-wheels. Blackthorn bushes shaped by the wind. Constellations (when he was 79, he wrote down on a January night 'I saw Orion upside-down in a pool of water under an oak'). Bells on New Year's Eve ringing the Old Year out and the New Year in. Rain across the view, and drops of water hanging from leaves and gates. Winter especially, and the different look things and people have in winter, in frost, or in snow. Dying light in the evening, which creates a strangeness in familiar things (on one occasion he noticed how such light made holly leaves 'shine like human eyes').

He said in winter the landscape changes from a picture to an engraving. He liked stories about frost and ice: 'Heard of an open cart being driven through the freezing rain. The people in it became literally packed in ice; the men's beards and hair were hung with icicles. Getting one of the men into the house was like bringing in a chandelier of lustres.'

When Hardy went for a walk natural things such as trees often seemed to him like beings who were solemnly thinking and thinking, but not able to speak. Sometimes they could speak, after all: '*New Year's Eve.* Looked out of doors just before twelve, and was confronted by the timeless white of the snow spread in front, against which stood the row of pines breathing out: "'Tis no better with us than with the rest of creation, you see!"'

Last of all, what did Hardy himself look like? I think as a rule only poets who pretend, look 'poetical'. Remember Emma Hardy, Emma Gifford, noticing in her future husband, when she saw him first, a 'business appearance'. Hardy never looked pompous or important. He was not very tall, just over five foot six inches; he was slight. Till he turned 50 (when he still appeared young and fresh, without wrinkles, though his hair had retreated from his young forehead), he wore a short beard and sidewhiskers: he had dark eyebrows, and blue-grey eyes; his fingers were long. He often looked a little sad, but he could smile very sweetly; and he moved in a quick birdlike way (he always loved dancing).

When he died in 1928, they buried his ashes – he was so famous, for his novels, at any rate, as I have said – in Westminster Abbey, in the Poets' Corner. Two of the pall-bearers were the Prime Minister of the day and another eminent politician – one Conservative, one Labour. That would have amused him.

Before his body was cremated, his heart had been taken out for burial in Emma Hardy's grave at Stinsford. Granted that his ashes were to rest in the Abbey, I think Hardy would have approved of that operation and its purpose: he would have liked the symbolism, the old, old idea that love comes from the heart, though the separate burial of a heart does seem a barbaric, medieval custom for our twentieth century.

It is said that his heart was kept in the parlour-maid's biscuit tin in the house at Max Gate, until it was buried. That certainly would have entertained him. Hardy himself had always collected such bizarre details about life and death.

GEOFFREY GRIGSON

THE NIGHT OF TRAFALGÁR

I

IN the wild October night-time, when the wind raved round the land,
And the Back-sea[1] met the Front-sea, and our doors were blocked with sand,
And we heard the drub of Dead-man's Bay, where bones of thousands are,
We knew not what the day had done for us at Trafalgár.
                    (All)   Had done,
                            Had done,
                    For us at Trafalgár!

II

'Pull hard, and make the Nothe, or down we go!' one says, says he.
We pulled; and bedtime brought the storm; but snug at home slept we.
Yet all the while our gallants after fighting through the day,
Were beating up and down the dark, sou'-west of Cadiz Bay.
                    The dark,
                    The dark,
            Sou'-west of Cadiz Bay!

III

The victors and the vanquished then the storm it tossed and tore,
As hard they strove, those worn-out men, upon that surly shore;
Dead Nelson and his half-dead crew, his foes from near and far,
Were rolled together on the deep that night at Trafalgár!
                    The deep
                    The deep,
            That night at Trafalgár!

[1] In those days the hind-part of the harbour adjoining this scene was so named, and at
high tides the waves washed across the isthmus at a point called 'The Narrows.'

SHORTENING DAYS AT THE HOMESTEAD

THE first fire since the summer is lit, and is smoking into the room:
   The sun-rays thread it through, like woof-lines in a loom.
   Sparrows spurt from the hedge, whom misgivings appal
That winter did not leave last year for ever, after all.
      Like shock-headed urchins, spiny-haired,
      Stand pollard willows, their twigs just bared.

      Who is this coming with pondering pace,
      Black and ruddy, with white embossed,
      His eyes being black, and ruddy his face
      And the marge of his hair like morning frost?
         It's the cider-maker,
         And appletree-shaker,
      And behind him on wheels, in readiness,
      His mill, and tubs, and vat, and press.

THE OXEN

CHRISTMAS Eve, and twelve of the clock.
  'Now they are all on their knees,'
An elder said as we sat in a flock
  By the embers in hearthside ease.

We pictured the meek mild creatures where
  They dwelt in their strawy pen,
Nor did it occur to one of us there
  To doubt they were kneeling then.

So fair a fancy few would weave
  In these years! Yet, I feel,
If someone said on Christmas Eve,
  'Come; see the oxen kneel

'In the lonely barton by yonder coomb
  Our childhood used to know,'
I should go with him in the gloom,
  Hoping it might be so.

TO THE MOON

'WHAT have you looked at, Moon,
    In your time,
  Now long past your prime?'
'O, I have looked at, often looked at
    Sweet, sublime,
Sore things, shudderful, night and noon
    In my time.'

  'What have you mused on, Moon,
    In your day,
  So aloof, so far away?'
'O, I have mused on, often mused on
    Growth, decay,
Nations alive, dead, mad, aswoon,
    In my day!'

  'Have you much wondered, Moon,
    On your rounds,
  Self-wrapt, beyond Earth's bounds?'
'Yea, I have wondered, often wondered
    At the sounds
Reaching me of the human tune
    On my rounds.'

  'What do you think of it, Moon,
    As you go?
  Is Life much, or no?'
'O, I think of it, often think of it
    As a show
God ought surely to shut up soon,
    As I go.'

THE ROMAN ROAD

THE Roman Road runs straight and bare
As the pale parting-line in hair
Across the heath. And thoughtful men
Contrast its days of Now and Then,
And delve, and measure, and compare;

Visioning on the vacant air
Helmed legionaries, who proudly rear
The Eagle, as they pace again
                The Roman Road.

But no tall brass-helmed legionnaire
Haunts it for me. Uprises there
A mother's form upon my ken,
Guiding my infant steps, as when
We walked that ancient thoroughfare,
                The Roman Road.

FRIENDS BEYOND

WILLIAM DEWY, Tranter Reuben, Farmer Ledlow late at plough,
　　　Robert's kin, and John's, and Ned's,
And the Squire, and Lady Susan, lie in Mellstock churchyard now!

'Gone,' I call them, gone for good, that group of local hearts and heads;
　　　Yet at mothy curfew-tide,
And at midnight when the noon-heat breathes it back from walls and leads,

They've a way of whispering to me – fellow-wight who yet abide –
　　　In the muted, measured note
Of a ripple under archways, or a lone cave's stillicide:

'We have triumphed: this achievement turns the bane to antidote,
　　　Unsuccesses to success,
Many thought-worn eves and morrows to a morrow free of thought.

'No more need we corn and clothing, feel of old terrestial stress;
　　　Chill detraction stirs no sigh;
Fear of death has even bygone us: death gave all that we possess.'

W. D. 'Ye mid burn the old bass-viol that I set such value by.'
Squire. 'You may hold the manse in fee,
　　　You may wed my spouse, may let my children's memory of me die.'

Lady S. 'You may have my rich brocades, my laces; take each household key;
　　　Ransack coffer, desk, bureau;
Quiz the few poor treasures hid there, con the letters kept by me.'

Far. 'Ye mid zell my favourite heifer, ye mid let the charlock grow,
　　　Foul the grinterns, give up thrift.'
Far. Wife. 'If ye break my best blue china, children, I shan't care or ho.'

All. 'We've no wish to hear the tidings, how the people's fortunes shift;
    What your daily doings are;
  Who are wedded, born, divided; if your lives beat slow or swift.

'Curious not the least are we if our intents you make or mar,
    If you quire to our old tune,
If the City stage still passes, if the weirs still roar afar.'

– Thus, with very gods' composure, freed those crosses late and soon
    Which, in life, the Trine allow
(Why, none witteth), and ignoring all that haps beneath the moon,

William Dewy, Tranter Reuben, Farmer Ledlow late at plough,
    Robert's kin, and John's, and Ned's,
And the Squire, and Lady Susan, murmur mildly to me now.

A BIRD-SCENE AT A RURAL DWELLING

WHEN the inmate stirs, the birds retire discreetly
From the window-ledge, whereon they whistled sweetly
    And on the step of the door,
    In the misty morning hoar;
  But now the dweller is up they flee
  To the crooked neighbouring codlin-tree;
And when he comes fully forth they seek the garden,
And call from the lofty costard, as pleading pardon
    For shouting so near before
    In their joy at being alive:–
Meanwhile the hammering clock within goes five.

I know a domicile of brown and green,
Where for a hundred summers there have been
Just such enactments, just such daybreaks seen.

A CHURCH ROMANCE

Mellstock : circa 1835

SHE turned in the high pew, until her sight
Swept the west gallery, and caught its row
Of music-men with viol, book, and bow
Against the sinking sad tower-window light.

She turned again; and in her pride's despite
One strenuous viol's inspirer seemed to throw
A message from his string to her below,
Which said: 'I claim thee as my own forthright!'

Thus their hearts' bond began, in due time signed.
And long years thence, when Age had scared Romance,
At some old attitude of his or glance
That gallery-scene would break upon her mind,
With him as minstrel, ardent, young, and trim,
Bowing 'New Sabbath' or 'Mount Ephraim.'

A SHEEP FAIR

THE day arrives of the autumn fair,
   And torrents fall,
Though sheep in throngs are gathered there,
   Ten thousand all,
Sodden, with hurdles round them reared:
And, lot by lot, the pens are cleared,
And the auctioneer wrings out his beard,
And wipes his book, bedrenched and smeared,
And rakes the rain from his face with the edge of his hand,
   As torrents fall.

The wool of the ewes is like a sponge
   With the daylong rain:
Jammed tight, to turn, or lie, or lunge,
   They strive in vain.
Their horns are soft as finger-nails,
Their shepherds reek against the rails,
The tied dogs soak with tucked-in tails,
The buyers' hat-brims fill like pails,
Which spill small cascades when they shift their stand
   In the daylong rain.

POSTSCRIPT

Time has trailed lengthily since met
   At Pummery Fair
Those panting thousands in their wet
   And woolly wear:
And every flock long since has bled,
And all the dripping buyers have sped,
And the hoarse auctioneer is dead,
Who 'Going – going!' so often said,
As he consigned to doom each meek, mewed band
   At Pummery Fair.

A BROKEN APPOINTMENT

You did not come,
And marching Time drew on, and wore me numb. –
Yet less for loss of your dear presence there
Than that I thus found lacking in your make
That high compassion which can overbear
Reluctance for pure lovingkindness' sake
Grieved I, when, as the hope-hour stroked its sum,
You did not come.

You love not me,
And love alone can lend you loyalty;
– I know and knew it.   But, unto the store
Of human deeds divine in all but name,
Was it not worth a little hour or more
To add yet this: Once you, a woman, came
To soothe a time-torn man; even though it be
You love not me?

AT CASTERBRIDGE FAIR

THE BALLAD-SINGER

SING, Ballad-singer, raise a hearty tune;
Make me forget that there was ever a one
I walked with in the meek light of the moon
    When the day's work was done.

Rhyme, Ballad-rhymer, start a country song;
Make me forget that she whom I loved well
Swore she would love me dearly, love me long,
    Then – what I cannot tell!

Sing, Ballad-singer, from your little book;
Make me forget those heart-breaks, achings, fears;
Make me forget her name, her sweet sweet look –
    Make me forget her tears.

'REGRET NOT ME'

REGRET not me;
Beneath the sunny tree
I lie uncaring, slumbering peacefully.

Swift as the light
I flew my faery flight;
Ecstatically I moved, and feared no night.

I did not know
That heydays fade and go,
But deemed that what was would be always so.

I skipped at morn
Between the yellowing corn,
Thinking it good and glorious to be born.

I ran at eves
Among the piled-up sheaves,
Dreaming, 'I grieve not, therefore nothing grieves.'

Now soon will come
The apple, pear, and plum,
And hinds will sing, and autumn insects hum.

Again you will fare
To cider-makings rare,
And junketings; but I shall not be there.

Yet gaily sing
Until the pewter ring
Those songs we sang when we went gipsying.

And lightly dance
Some triple-timed romance
In coupled figures, and forget mischance;

And mourn not me
Beneath the yellowing tree;
For I shall mind not, slumbering peacefully.

IN TIME OF 'THE BREAKING OF NATIONS'

I

ONLY a man harrowing clods
    In a slow silent walk
With an old horse that stumbles and nods
    Half asleep as they stalk.

II

Only thin smoke without flame
    From the heaps of couch-grass;
Yet this will go onward the same
    Though Dynasties pass.

III

Yonder a maid and her wight
    Come whispering by:
War's annals will cloud into night
    Ere their story die.

1915

A TRAMPWOMAN'S TRAGEDY

I

FROM Wynyard's Gap the livelong day,
          The livelong day,
We beat afoot the northward way
          We had travelled times before.
The sun-blaze burning on our backs,
Our shoulders sticking to our packs,
By fosseway, fields, and turnpike tracks
          We skirted sad Sedge-Moor.

II

Full twenty miles we jaunted on,
          We jaunted on, –
My fancy-man, and jeering John,
          And Mother Lee, and I.
And, as the sun drew down to west,
We climbed the toilsome Poldon crest,
And saw, of landskip sights the best,
          The inn that beamed thereby.

III

For months we had padded side by side,
      Ay, side by side
Through the Great Forest, Blackmoor wide,
      And where the Parret ran.
We'd faced the gusts on Mendip ridge,
Had crossed the Yeo unhelped by bridge,
Been stung by every Marshwood midge,
      I and my fancy-man.

IV

Lone inns we loved, my man and I,
      My man and I;
'King's Stag,' 'Windwhistle' high and dry,
      'The Horse' on Hintock Green,
The cosy house at Wynyard's Gap,
'The Hut' renowned on Bredy Knap,
And many another wayside tap
      Where folk might sit unseen.

V

Now as we trudged – O deadly day,
      O deadly day! –
I teased my fancy-man in play
      And wanton idleness.
I walked alongside jeering John,
I laid his hand my waist upon;
I would not bend my glances on
      My lover's dark distress.

35

VI

Thus Poldon top at last we won,
   At last we won,
And gained the inn at sink of sun
   Far-famed as 'Marshal's Elm.'
Beneath us figured tor and lea,
From Mendip to the western sea –
I doubt if finer sight there be
   Within this royal realm.

VII

Inside the settle all a-row –
   All four a-row
We sat, I next to John, to show
   That he had wooed and won.
And then he took me on his knee,
And swore it was his turn to be
My favoured mate, and Mother Lee
   Passed to my former one.

VIII

Then in a voice I had never heard,
   I had never heard,
My only Love to me: 'One word,
   My lady, if you please!
Whose is the child you are like to bear? –
His? After all my months o' care?'
God knows 'twas not! But, O despair!
   I nodded – still to tease.

Then up he sprung, and with his knife –
        And with his knife
He let out jeering Johnny's life,
        Yes; there, at set of sun.
The slant ray through the window nigh
Gilded John's blood and glazing eye,
Ere scarcely Mother Lee and I
        Knew that the deed was done.

X

The taverns tell the gloomy tale,
        The gloomy tale,
How that at Ivel-chester jail
        My Love, my sweetheart swung;
Though stained till now by no misdeed
Save one horse ta'en in time o' need;
(Blue Jimmy stole right many a steed
        Ere his last fling he flung.)

XI

Thereaft I walked the world alone,
        Alone, alone!
On his death-day I gave my groan
        And dropt his dead-born child.
'Twas nigh the jail, beneath a tree,
None tending me; for Mother Lee
Had died at Glaston, leaving me
        Unfriended on the wild.

XII

And in the night as I lay weak,
      As I lay weak,
The leaves a-falling on my cheek,
      The red moon low declined –
The ghost of him I'd die to kiss
Rose up and said: 'Ah, tell me this!
Was the child mine, or was it his?
      Speak, that I rest may find!'

XIII

O doubt not but I told him then,
      I told him then,
That I had kept me from all men
      Since we joined lips and swore.
Whereat he smiled, and thinned away
As the wind stirred to call up day ...
– 'Tis past! And here alone I stray
      Haunting the Western Moor.

'WHEN I SET OUT FOR LYONNESSE'

When I set out for Lyonnesse,
    A hundred miles away,
    The rime was on the spray,
And starlight lit my lonesomeness
When I set out for Lyonnesse
    A hundred miles away.

What would bechance at Lyonnesse
    While I should sojourn there
    No prophet durst declare,
Nor did the wisest wizard guess
What would bechance at Lyonnesse
    While I should sojourn there.

When I came back from Lyonnesse
    With magic in my eyes,
    All marked with mute surmise
My radiance rare and fathomless,
When I came back from Lyonnesse
    With magic in my eyes!

'A MAN WAS DRAWING NEAR TO ME'

On that gray night of mournful drone,
Apart from aught to hear, to see,
I dreamt not that from shires unknown
    In gloom, alone,
    By Halworthy,
A man was drawing near to me.

I'd no concern at anything,
No sense of coming pull-heart play;
Yet, under the silent outspreading
    Of even's wing
    Where Otterham lay,
A man was riding up my way.

I thought of nobody – not of one,
But only of trifles – legends, ghosts –
Though, on the moorland dim and dun
    That travellers shun
    About these coasts,
The man had passed Tresparret Posts.

There was no light at all inland,
Only the seaward pharos-fire,
Nothing to let me understand
    That hard at hand
    By Hennett Byre
The man was getting nigh and nigher.

There was a rumble at the door,
A draught disturbed the drapery,
And but a minute passed before,
    With gaze that bore
    My destiny,
The man revealed himself to me.

AT THE WORD 'FAREWELL'

SHE looked like a bird from a cloud
    On the clammy lawn,
Moving alone, bare-browed
    In the dim of dawn.
The candles alight in the room
    For my parting meal
Made all things withoutdoors loom
    Strange, ghostly, unreal.

The hour itself was a ghost,
    And it seemed to me then
As of chances the chance furthermost
    I should see her again.
I beheld not where all was so fleet
    That a Plan of the past
Which had ruled us from birthtime to meet
    Was in working at last:

No prelude did I there perceive
    To a drama at all,
Or foreshadow what fortune might weave
    From beginnings so small;
But I rose as if quicked by a spur
    I was bound to obey,
And stepped through the casement to her
    Still alone in the gray.

'I am leaving you. . . . Farewell!' I said,
    As I followed her on
By an alley bare boughs overspread;
    'I soon must be gone!'
Even then the scale might have been turned
    Against love by a feather –
But crimson one cheek of hers burned
    When we came in together.

A THUNDERSTORM IN TOWN

A Reminiscence : 1893

SHE wore a new 'terra-cotta' dress,
And we stayed, because of the pelting storm,
Within the hansom's dry recess,
Though the horse had stopped; yea, motionless
     We sat on, snug and warm.

Then the downpour ceased, to my sharp sad pain
And the glass that had screened our forms before
Flew up, and out she sprang to her door:
I should have kissed her if the rain
     Had lasted a minute more.

WHERE THEY LIVED

DISHEVELLED leaves creep down
Upon that bank to-day,
Some green, some yellow, and some pale brown;
The wet bents bob and sway;
The once warm slippery turf is sodden
Where we laughingly sat or lay.

The summerhouse is gone,
Leaving a weedy space;
The bushes that veiled it once have grown
Gaunt trees that interlace,
Through whose lank limbs I see too clearly
The nakedness of the place.

And where were hills of blue,
Blind drifts of vapour blow,
And the names of former dwellers few,
If any, people know,
And instead of a voice that called, 'Come in, Dears.'
Time calls, 'Pass below!'

'AND THERE WAS A GREAT CALM'

ON THE SIGNING OF THE ARMISTICE, 11 NOV. 1918

I

THERE had been years of Passion – scorching, cold,
And much Despair, and Anger heaving high,
Care whitely watching, Sorrows manifold,
Among the young, among the weak and old,
And the pensive Spirit of Pity whispered, 'Why?'

II

Men had not paused to answer. Foes distraught
Pierced the thinned peoples in a brute-like blindness,
Philosophies that sages long had taught,
And Selflessness, were as an unknown thought,
And 'Hell!' and 'Shell!' were yapped at Lovingkindness.

III

The feeble folk at home had grown full-used
To 'dug-outs,' 'snipers,' 'Huns,' from the war-adept
In the mornings heard, and at evetides perused;
To day-dreamt men in millions, when they mused –
To nightmare-men in millions when they slept.

IV

Waking to wish existence timeless, null,
Sirius they watched above where armies fell;
He seemed to check his flapping when, in the lull
Of night a boom came thencewise, like the dull
Plunge of a stone dropped into some deep well.

V

So, when old hopes that earth was bettering slowly
Were dead and damned, there sounded 'War is done!'
One morrow. Said the bereft, and meek, and lowly,
'Will men some day be given to grace? yea, wholly,
And in good sooth, as our dreams used to run?'

VI

Breathless they paused. Out there men raised their glance
To where had stood those poplars lank and lopped,
As they had raised it through the four years' dance
Of Death in the now familiar flats of France;
And murmured, 'Strange, this! How? All firing stopped?'

VII

Aye; all was hushed. The about-to-fire fired not,
The aimed-at moved away in trance-lipped song.
One checkless regiment slung a clinching shot
And turned. The Spirit of Irony smirked out, 'What?
Spoil peradventures woven of Rage and Wrong?'

VIII

Thenceforth no flying fires inflamed the gray,
No hurtlings shook the dewdrop from the thorn,
No moan perplexed the mute bird on the spray;
Worn horses mused: 'We are not whipped today';
No weft-winged engines blurred the moon's thin horn.

IX

Calm fell. From Heaven distilled a clemency;
There was peace on earth, and silence in the sky;
Some could, some could not, shake off misery:
The Sinister Spirit sneered: 'It had to be!'
And again the Spirit of Pity whispered, 'Why?'

ON STURMINSTER FOOT-BRIDGE

Onomatopoeic

R E T I C U L A T I O N S creep upon the slack stream's face
    When the wind skims irritably past,
The current clucks smartly into each hollow place
That years of flood have scrabbled in the pier's sodden base;
    The floating-lily leaves rot fast.

On a roof stand the swallows ranged in wistful waiting rows,
    Till they arrow off and drop like stones
Among the eyot-withies at whose foot the river flows:
And beneath the roof is she who in the dark world shows
    As a lattice-gleam when midnight moans.

AT A COUNTRY FAIR

At a bygone Western country fair
I saw a giant led by a dwarf
With a red string like a long thin scarf;
How much he was the stronger there
     The giant seemed unaware.

And then I saw that the giant was blind,
And the dwarf a shrewd-eyed little thing;
The giant, mild, timid, obeyed the string
As if he had no independent mind,
     Or will of any kind.

Wherever the dwarf decided to go
At his heels the other trotted meekly,
(Perhaps – I know not – reproaching weakly)
Like one Fate bade that it must be so,
     Whether he wished or no.

Various sights in various climes
I have seen, and more I may see yet,
But that sight never shall I forget,
And have thought it the sorriest of pantomimes,
     If once, a hundred times!

AT THE RAILWAY STATION, UPWAY

'THERE is not much that I can do,
  For I've no money that's quite my own!'
  Spoke up the pitying child –
A little boy with a violin
At the station before the train came in, –
'But I can play my fiddle to you,
And a nice one 'tis, and good in tone!'

  The man in the handcuffs smiled;
The constable looked, and he smiled, too,
  As the fiddle began to twang;
And the man in the handcuffs suddenly sang
      With grimful glee:
      'This life so free
      Is the thing for me!'
And the constable smiled, and said no word,
As if unconscious of what he heard;
And so they went on till the train came in –
The convict, and boy with the violin.

NO BUYERS

A STREET SCENE

A LOAD of brushes and baskets and cradles and chairs
    Labours along the street in the rain:
With it a man, a woman, a pony with whiteybrown hairs. –
    The man foots in front of the horse with a shambling sway
      At a slower tread than a funeral train,
    While to a dirge-like tune he chants his wares,
Swinging a Turk's-head brush (in a drum-major's way
      When the bandsmen march and play).

A yard from the back of the man is the whiteybrown pony's nose:
He mirrors his master in every item of pace and pose:
    He stops when the man stops, without being told,
    And seems to be eased by a pause; too plainly he's old,
      Indeed, not strength enough shows
    To steer the disjointed waggon straight,
    Which wriggles left and right in a rambling line,
    Deflected thus by its own warp and weight,
    And pushing the pony with it in each incline.

    The woman walks on the pavement verge,
      Parallel to the man:
She wears an apron white and wide in span,
And carries a like Turk's-head, but more in nursing-wise:
      Now and then she joins in his dirge,
      But as if her thoughts were on distant things.
      The rain clams her apron till it clings. –
    So, step by step, they move with their merchandize,
      And nobody buys.

SNOW IN THE SUBURBS

EVERY branch big with it,
  Bent every twig with it;
Every fork like a white web-foot;
Every street and pavement mute:
Some flakes have lost their way, and grope back upward, when
Meeting those meandering down they turn and descend again.
  The palings are glued together like a wall,
  And there is no waft of wind with the fleecy fall.

  A sparrow enters the tree,
  Whereon immediately
A snow-lump thrice his own slight size
Descends on him and showers his head and eyes,
  And overturns him,
  And near inurns him,
And lights on a nether twig, when its brush
Starts off a volley of other lodging lumps with a rush.

  The steps are a blanched slope,
  Up which, with feeble hope,
A black cat comes, wide-eyed and thin;
    And we take him in.

TO AN UNBORN PAUPER CHILD

I

BREATHE not, hid Heart: cease silently,
And though thy birth-hour beckons thee,
    Sleep the long sleep:
    The Doomsters heap
Travails and teens around us here,
And Time-wraiths turn our songsingings to fear.

II

Hark, how the peoples surge and sigh,
And laughters fail, and greetings die:
    Hopes dwindle; yea,
    Faiths waste away,
Affections and enthusiasms numb;
Thou canst not mend these things if thou dost come.

III

Had I the ear of wombèd souls
Ere their terrestrial chart unrolls,
    And thou wert free
    To cease, or be,
Then would I tell thee all I know,
And put it to thee: Wilt thou take Life so?

IV

Vain vow! No hint of mine may hence
To theeward fly: to thy locked sense
    Explain none can
    Life's pending plan:
Thou wilt thy ignorant entry make
Though skies spout fire and blood and nations quake.

Fain would I, dear, find some shut plot
Of earth's wide wold for thee, where not
    One tear, one qualm,
    Should break the calm.
But I am weak as thou and bare;
No man can change the common lot to rare.

Must come and bide. And such are we –
Unreasoning, sanguine, visionary –
    That I can hope
    Health, love, friends, scope
In full for thee; can dream thou'lt find
Joys seldom yet attained by humankind!

THE SELF-UNSEEING

HERE is the ancient floor,
Footworn and hollowed and thin,
Here was the former door
Where the dead feet walked in.

She sat here in her chair,
Smiling into the fire;
He who played stood there,
Bowing it higher and higher.

Childlike, I danced in a dream;
Blessings emblazoned that day;
Everything glowed with a gleam;
Yet we were looking away!

THROWING A TREE

THE two executioners stalk along over the knolls,
Bearing two axes with heavy heads shining and wide,
And a long limp two-handled saw toothed for cutting great boles,
And so they approach the proud tree that bears the death-mark on its side.

Jackets doffed they swing axes and chop away just above ground,
And the chips fly about and lie white on the moss and fallen leaves;
Till a broad deep gash in the bark is hewn all the way round,
And one of them tries to hook upward a rope, which at last he achieves.

The saw then begins, till the top of the tall giant shivers;
The shivers are seen to grow greater each cut than before:
They edge out the saw, tug the rope; but the tree only quivers,
And kneeling and sawing again, they step back to try pulling once more.

Then, lastly, the living mast sways, further sways: with a shout
Job and Ike rush aside. Reached the end of its long staying powers
The tree crashes downward: it shakes all its neighbours throughout,
And two hundred years' steady growth has been ended in less than two hours.

OVERLOOKING THE RIVER STOUR

THE swallows flew in the curves of an eight
   Above the river-gleam
   In the wet June's last beam:
Like little crossbows animate
The swallows flew in the curves of an eight
   Above the river-gleam.

Planing up shavings of crystal spray
   A moor-hen darted out
   From the bank thereabout,
And through the stream-shine ripped his way;
Planing up shavings of crystal spray
   A moor-hen darted out.

Closed were the kingcups; and the mead
   Dripped in monotonous green,
   Though the day's morning sheen
Had shown it golden and honeybee'd;
Closed were the kingcups; and the mead
   Dripped in monotonous green.

And never I turned my head, alack,
   While these things met my gaze
   Through the pane's drop-drenched glaze,
To see the more behind my back. . . .
O never I turned, but let, alack,
   These less things hold my gaze!

AN AUGUST MIDNIGHT

I

A SHADED lamp and a waving blind,
And the beat of a clock from a distant floor:
On this scene enter – winged, horned, and spined –
A longlegs, a moth, and a dumbledore;
While 'mid my page there idly stands
A sleepy fly, that rubs its hands ...

II

Thus meet we five, in this still place,
At this point of time, at this point in space.
– My guests besmear my new-penned line,
Or bang at the lamp and fall supine.
'God's humblest, they!' I muse.   Yet why?
They know Earth-secrets that know not I.

LAUSANNE

IN GIBBON'S OLD GARDEN: 11-12 P.M.
June 27, 1897[1]

A SPIRIT seems to pass,
Formal in pose, but grave withal and grand:
He contemplates a volume in his hand,
And far lamps fleck him through the thin acacias.

Anon the book is closed,
With 'It is finished!' And at the alley's end
He turns, and when on me his glances bend
As from the Past comes speech – small, muted, yet composed.

'How fares the Truth now? – Ill?
– Do pens but slily further her advance?
May one not speed her but in phrase askance?
Do scribes aver the Comic to be Reverend still?

'Still rule those minds on earth
At whom sage Milton's wormwood words were hurled:
"Truth like a bastard comes into the world
Never without ill-fame to him who gives her birth"?'

---

[1] The 110th anniversary of the completion of the 'Decline and Fall' at the same hour and place.

THE DARKLING THRUSH

I LEANT upon a coppice gate
    When Frost was spectre-gray,
And Winter's dregs made desolate
    The weakening eye of day.
The tangled bine-stems scored the sky
    Like strings of broken lyres,
And all mankind that haunted nigh
    Had sought their household fires.

The land's sharp features seemed to be
    The Century's corpse outleant,
His crypt the cloudy canopy,
    The wind his death-lament.
The ancient pulse of germ and birth
    Was shrunken hard and dry,
And every spirit upon earth
    Seemed fervourless as I.

At once a voice arose among
    The bleak twigs overhead
In a full-hearted evensong
    Of joy illimited;
An aged thrush, frail, gaunt, and small,
    In blast-beruffled plume,
Had chosen thus to fling his soul
    Upon the growing gloom.

So little cause for carolings
    Of such ecstatic sound
Was written on terrestrial things
    Afar or nigh around,
That I could think there trembled through
    His happy good-night air
Some blessed Hope, whereof he knew
    And I was unaware.

31st December 1900

WAITING BOTH

A STAR looks down at me,
And says: 'Here I and you
Stand, each in our degree:
What do you mean to do, –
Mean to do?'

I say: 'For all I know,
Wait, and let Time go by,
Till my change come.' – 'Just so,'
The star says: 'So mean I:–
So mean I.'

LYING AWAKE

You, Morningtide Star, now are steady-eyed, over the east,
I know it as if I saw you;
You, Beeches, engrave on the sky your thin twigs, even the least;
Had I paper and pencil I'd draw you.

You, Meadow, are white with your counterpane cover of dew,
I see it as if I were there;
You, Churchyard, are lightening faint from the shade of the yew,
The names creeping out everywhere.

AFTERNOON SERVICE AT MELLSTOCK

Circa 1850

On afternoons of drowsy calm
 We stood in the panelled pew,
Singing one-voiced a Tate-and-Brady psalm
 To the tune of 'Cambridge New.'

We watched the elms, we watched the rooks,
 The clouds upon the breeze,
Between the whiles of glancing at our books,
 And swaying like the trees.

So mindless were those outpourings! –
 Though I am not aware
That I have gained by subtle thought on things
 Since we stood psalming there.

NOBODY COMES

Tʀᴇᴇ-ʟᴇᴀᴠᴇs labour up and down,
    And through them the fainting light
    Succumbs to the crawl of night.
Outside in the road the telegraph wire
    To the town from the darkening land
Intones to travellers like a spectral lyre
    Swept by a spectral hand.

A car comes up, with lamps full-glare,
    That flash upon a tree:
    It has nothing to do with me,
And whangs along in a world of its own,
    Leaving a blacker air;
And mute by the gate I stand again alone,
    And nobody pulls up there.

THE HARBOUR BRIDGE

FROM here, the quay, one looks above to mark
The bridge across the harbour, hanging dark
Against the day's-end sky, fair-green in glow
Over and under the middle archway's bow:
It draws its skeleton where the sun has set,
Yea, clear from cutwater to parapet;
On which mild glow, too, lines of rope and spar
    Trace themselves black as char.

Down here in shade we hear the painters shift
Against the bollards with a drowsy lift,
As moved by the incoming stealthy tide.
High up across the bridge the burghers glide
As cut black-paper portraits hastening on
In conversation none knows what upon:
Their sharp-edged lips move quickly word by word
    To speech that is not heard.

There trails the dreamful girl, who leans and stops,
There presses the practical woman to the shops,
There is a sailor, meeting his wife with a start,
And we, drawn nearer, judge they are keeping apart.
Both pause. She says: 'I've looked for you. I thought
We'd make it up.' Then no words can be caught.
At last: 'Won't you come home?' She moves still nigher:
    ' 'Tis comfortable, with a fire.'

'No,' he says gloomily. 'And, anyhow,
I can't give up the other woman now:
You should have talked like that in former days,
When I was last home.' They go different ways.
And the west dims, and yellow lamplights shine:
And soon above, like lamps more opaline,
White stars ghost forth, that care not for men's wives,
    Or any other lives.

Weymouth

LIFE AND DEATH AT SUNRISE

NEAR DOGBURY GATE, 1867

THE hills uncap their tops
Of woodland, pasture, copse,
And look on the layers of mist
At their foot that still persist:
They are like awakened sleepers on one elbow lifted,
Who gaze around to learn if things during night have shifted.

A waggon creaks up from the fog
With a laboured leisurely jog;
Then a horseman from off the hill-tip
Comes clapping down into the dip;
While woodlarks, finches, sparrows, try to entune at one time,
And cocks and hens and cows and bulls take up the chime.

With a shouldered basket and flagon
A man meets the one with the waggon,
And both the men halt of long use.
'Well,' the waggoner says, 'what's the news?'
'– 'Tis a boy this time. You've just met the doctor trotting back.
She's doing very well. And we think we shall call him "Jack."

'And what have you got covered there?'
He nods to the waggon and mare.
'Oh, a coffin for old John Thinn:
We are just going to put him in.'
'– So he's gone at last. He always had a good constitution.'
'– He was ninety-odd. He could call up the French Revolution.'

67

THE FIVE STUDENTS

THE sparrow dips in his wheel-rut bath,
    The sun grows passionate-eyed,
And boils the dew to smoke by the paddock-path;
    As strenuously we stride, –
Five of us; dark He, fair He, dark She, fair She, I,
    All beating by.

The air is shaken, the high-road hot,
    Shadowless swoons the day,
The greens are sobered and cattle at rest; but not
    We on our urgent way, –
Four of us; fair She, dark She, fair He, I, are there,
    But one – elsewhere.

Autumn moulds the hard fruit mellow,
    And forward still we press
Through moors, briar-meshed plantations, clay-pits yellow,
    As in the spring hours – yes,
Three of us; fair He, fair She, I, as heretofore,
    But – fallen one more.

The leaf drops: earthworms draw it in
    At night-time noiselessly,
The fingers of birch and beech are skeleton-thin,
    And yet on the beat are we, –
Two of us; fair She, I. But no more left to go
    The track we know.

Icicles tag the church-aisle leads,
  The flag-rope gibbers hoarse,
The home-bound foot-folk wrap their snow-flaked heads,
  Yet I still stalk the course –
One of us. . . . Dark and fair He, dark and fair She, gone:
  The rest – anon.

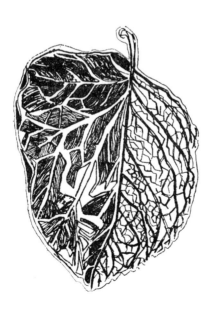

THE MOCK WIFE

It's a dark drama, this; and yet I know the house, and date;
That is to say, the where and when John Channing met his fate.
The house was one in High Street, seen of burghers still alive,
The year was some two centuries bygone; seventeen-hundred and five.

And dying was Channing the grocer. All the clocks had struck eleven,
And the watchers saw that ere the dawn his soul would be in Heaven;
When he said on a sudden: 'I should *like* to kiss her before I go, –
For one last time!' They looked at each other and murmured, 'Even so.'

She'd just been haled to prison, his wife; yea, charged with shaping his death:
By poison, 'twas told; and now he was nearing the moment of his last breath:
He, witless that his young housemate was suspect of such a crime,
Lay thinking that his pangs were but a malady of the time.

Outside the room they pondered gloomily, wondering what to do,
As still he craved her kiss – the dying man who nothing knew:
'Guilty she may not be,' they said; 'so why should we torture him
In these his last few minutes of life? Yet how indulge his whim?'

And as he begged there piteously for what could not be done,
And the murder-charge had flown about the town to every one,
The friends around him in their trouble thought of a hasty plan,
And straightway set about it. Let denounce them all who can.

'O will you do a kindly deed – it may be a soul to save;
At least, great misery to a man with one foot in the grave?'
Thus they to the buxom woman not unlike his prisoned wife;
'The difference he's past seeing; it will soothe his sinking life.'

Well, the friendly neighbour did it; and he kissed her; held her fast;
Kissed her again and yet again. 'I – knew she'd – come at last! –
Where have you been? – Ah, kept away! – I'm sorry – overtried –
God bless you!' And he loosed her, fell back tiredly, and died.

His wife stood six months after on the scaffold before the crowd,
Ten thousand of them gathered there; fixed, silent, and hard-browed,
To see her strangled and burnt to dust, as was the verdict then
On women truly judged, or false, of doing to death their men.

Some of them said as they watched her burn: 'I am glad he never knew,
Since a few hold her as innocent – think such she could not do!
Glad, too, that (as they tell) he thought she kissed him ere he died.'
And they seemed to make no question that the cheat was justified.

ONCE AT SWANAGE

THE spray sprang up across the cusps of the moon,
  And all its light loomed green
  As a witch-flame's weirdsome sheen
At the minute of an incantation scene;
And it greened our gaze – that night at demilune.

Roaring high and roaring low was the sea
  Behind the headland shores:
  It symboled the slamming of doors,
Of a regiment hurrying over hollow floors. . . .
And there we two stood, hands clasped; I and she!

NIGHT-TIME IN MID-FALL

IT is a storm-strid night, winds footing swift
      Through the blind profound;
  I know the happenings from their sound;
Leaves totter down still green, and spin and drift;
The tree-trunks rock to their roots, which wrench and lift
The loam where they run onward underground.

The streams are muddy and swollen; eels migrate
      To a new abode;
  Even cross, 'tis said, the turnpike-road;
(Men's feet have felt their crawl, home-coming late):
The westward fronts of towers are saturate,
Church-timbers crack, and witches ride abroad.

DURING WIND AND RAIN

THEY sing their dearest songs –
He, she, all of them – yea,
Treble and tenor and bass,
    And one to play;
With the candles mooning each face. . . .
    Ah, no; the years O!
How the sick leaves reel down in throngs!

They clear the creeping moss –
Elders and juniors – aye,
Making the pathways neat
    And the garden gay;
And they build a shady seat. . . .
    Ah, no; the years, the years;
See, the white storm-birds wing across!

They are blithely breakfasting all –
Men and maidens – yea,
Under the summer tree,
    With a glimpse of the bay,
While pet fowl come to the knee. . . .
    Ah, no; the years O!
And the rotten rose is ript from the wall.

DRAWING DETAILS IN AN OLD CHURCH

I HEAR the bell-rope sawing,
And the oil-less axle grind,
As I sit alone here drawing
What some Gothic brain designed;
And I catch the toll that follows
  From the lagging bell,
Ere it spreads to hills and hollows
  Where people dwell.

I ask not whom it tolls for,
Incurious who he be;
So, some morrow, when those knolls for
One unguessed, sound out for me,
A stranger, loitering under
  In nave or choir,
May think, too, 'Whose, I wonder?'
  But not inquire.

THE VOICE

WOMAN much missed, how you call to me, call to me,
Saying that now you are not as you were
When you had changed from the one who was all to me,
But as at first, when our day was fair.

Can it be you that I hear? Let me view you, then,
Standing as when I drew near to the town
Where you would wait for me: yes, as I knew you then,
Even to the original air-blue gown!

Or is it only the breeze, in its listlessness
Travelling across the wet mead to me here,
You being ever dissolved to existlessness,
Heard no more again far or near?

Thus I; faltering forward,
Leaves around me falling,
Wind oozing thin through the thorn from norward,
And the woman calling.

AFTER A JOURNEY

HERETO I come to view a voiceless ghost;
  Whither, O whither will its whim now draw me?
Up the cliff, down, till I'm lonely, lost,
  And the unseen waters' ejaculations awe me.
Where you will next be there's no knowing,
  Facing round about me everywhere,
      With your nut-coloured hair,
And gray eyes, and rose-flush coming and going.

Yes: I have re-entered your olden haunts at last;
  Through the years, through the dead scenes I have tracked you;
What have you now found to say of our past –
  Scanned across the dark space wherein I have lacked you?
Summer gave us sweets, but autumn wrought division?
  Things were not lastly as firstly well
      With us twain, you tell?
But all's closed now, despite Time's derision.

I see what you are doing: you are leading me on
  To the spots we knew when we haunted here together,
The waterfall, above which the mist-bow shone
  At the then fair hour in the then fair weather,
And the cave just under, with a voice still so hollow
  That it seems to call out to me from forty years ago,
      When you were all aglow,
And not the thin ghost that I now frailly follow!

Ignorant of what there is flitting here to see,
    The waked birds preen and the seals flop lazily;
Soon you will have, Dear, to vanish from me,
    For the stars close their shutters and the dawn whitens hazily.
Trust me, I mind not, though Life lours,
    The bringing me here; nay, bring me here again!
        I am just the same as when
Our days were a joy, and our paths through flowers.

Pentargan Bay

THE PHANTOM HORSEWOMAN

I

QUEER are the ways of a man I know:
      He comes and stands
      In a careworn craze,
      And looks at the sands
      And the seaward haze
      With moveless hands
      And face and gaze,
      Then turns to go . . .
And what does he see when he gazes so?

II

They say he sees as an instant thing
      More clear than to-day,
      A sweet soft scene
      That was once in play
      By that briny green;
      Yes, notes alway
      Warm, real, and keen,
      What his back years bring –
A phantom of his own figuring.

III

Of this vision of his they might say more:
      Not only there
      Does he see this sight,
      But everywhere
      In his brain – day, night,
      As if on the air
      It were drawn rose-bright –
      Yea, far from that shore
Does he carry this vision of heretofore:

79

A ghost-girl-rider. And though, toil-tried,
 He withers daily,
 Times touches her not,
 But she still rides gaily
 In his rapt thought
 On that shagged and shaly
 Atlantic spot,
 And as when first eyed
Draws rein and sings to the swing of the tide.

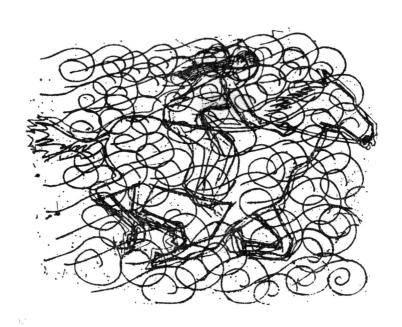

'IF YOU HAD KNOWN'

If you had known
When listening with her to the far-down moan
Of the white-selvaged and empurpled sea,
And rain came on that did not hinder talk,
Or damp your flashing facile gaiety
In turning home, despite the slow wet walk
By crooked ways, and over stiles of stone;
   If you had known

   You would lay roses,
Fifty years thence, on her monument, that discloses
Its graying shape upon the luxuriant green;
Fifty years thence to an hour, by chance led there,
What might have moved you? – yea, had you foreseen
That on the tomb of the selfsame one, gone where
The dawn of every day is as the close is,
   You would lay roses!

WHERE THE PICNIC WAS

WHERE we made the fire
In the summer time
Of branch and briar
On the hill to the sea,
I slowly climb
Through winter mire,
And scan and trace
The forsaken place
Quite readily.

Now a cold wind blows,
And the grass is gray,
But the spot still shows
As a burnt circle – aye,
And stick-ends, charred,
Still strew the sward
Whereon I stand,
Last relic of the band
Who came that day!

Yes, I am here
Just as last year,
And the sea breathes brine
From its strange straight line
Up hither, the same
As when we four came.
– But two have wandered far
From this grassy rise
Into urban roar
Where no picnics are,
And one – has shut her eyes
For evermore.

DAYS TO RECOLLECT

Do you recall
That day in Fall
When we walked towards Saint Alban's Head,
On thistledown that summer had shed,
Or must I remind you?
Winged thistle-seeds which hitherto
Had lain as none were there, or few,
But rose at the brush of your petticoat-seam
(As ghosts might rise of the recent dead),
And sailed on the breeze in a nebulous stream
Like a comet's tail behind you:
You don't recall
That day in Fall?

Then do you remember
That sad November
When you left me never to see me more,
And looked quite other than theretofore,
As if it could not *be* you?
And lay by the window whence you had gazed
So many times when blamed or praised,
Morning or noon, through years and years,
Accepting the gifts that Fortune bore,
Sharing, enduring, joys, hopes, fears!
Well: I never more did see you. –
Say you remember
That sad November!

'I SAID TO LOVE'

I SAID to Love,
'It is not now as in old days
When men adored thee and thy ways
　　　All else above;
Named thee the Boy, the Bright, the One
Who spread a heaven beneath the sun,'
　　　I said to Love.

I said to him,
'We now know more of thee than then;
We were but weak in judgment when,
　　　With hearts abrim,
We clamoured thee that thou would'st please
Inflict on us thine agonies,'
　　　I said to him.

I said to Love,
'Thou art not young, thou art not fair,
No elfin darts, no cherub air,
　　　Nor swan, nor dove
Are thine; but features pitiless,
And iron daggers of distress,'
　　　I said to Love.

　　　'Depart then, Love! . . .
– Man's race shall perish, threatenest thou,
Without thy kindling coupling-vow?
The age to come the man of now
　　　Know nothing of? –
We fear not such a threat from thee;
We are too old in apathy!
Mankind shall cease. – So let it be,'
　　　I said to Love.

THE GARDEN SEAT

Its former green is blue and thin,
And its once firm legs sink in and in;
Soon it will break down unaware,
Soon it will break down unaware.

At night when reddest flowers are black
Those who once sat thereon come back;
Quite a row of them sitting there,
Quite a row of them sitting there.

With them the seat does not break down,
Nor winter freeze them, nor floods drown,
For they are as light as upper air,
They are as light as upper air!

A LIGHT SNOW-FALL AFTER FROST

On the flat road a man at last appears:
How much his whitening hairs
Owe to the settling snow's mute anchorage,
And how much to a life's rough pilgrimage,
One cannot certify.

The frost is on the wane,
And cobwebs hanging close outside the pane
Pose as festoons of thick white worsted there,
Of their pale presence no eye being aware
Till the rime made them plain.

A second man comes by;
His ruddy beard brings fire to the pallid scene:
His coat is faded green;
Hence seems it that his mien
Wears something of the dye
Of the berried holm-trees that he passes nigh.

The snow-feathers so gently swoop that though
But half an hour ago
The road was brown, and now is starkly white,
A watcher would have failed defining quite
When it transformed it so.

Near Surbiton

IN SHERBORNE ABBEY
17—

THE moon has passed to the panes of the south-aisle wall,
And brought the mullioned shades and shines to fall
On the cheeks of a woman and man in a pew there, pressed
Together as they pant, and recline for rest.

Forms round them loom, recumbent like their own,
  Yet differing; for they are chiselled in frigid stone;
In doublets are some; some mailed, as whilom ashore they leapt:
And stately husbands and wives, side by side as they anciently slept.

'We are not like those,' she murmurs. 'For ever here set!'
'True, Love,' he replies. 'We two are not marble yet.'
  'And, worse,' said she; 'not husband and wife!'
  'But we soon shall be' (from him) 'if we've life!'
A silence. A trotting of horses is heard without.
The lovers scarce breathe till its echo has quite died out.

  'It was they! They have passed, anyhow!'
  'Our horse, slily hid by the conduit,
  They've missed, or they'd rushed to impound it!'
  'And they'll not discover us now.'
  'Will not, until 'tis too late.
  And we can outface them straight!'

'Why did you make me ride in your front?' says she.
'To outwit the law. That was my strategy.
  As I was borne off on the pillion behind you,
  Th'abductor was you, Dearest, let me remind you;
  And seizure of me by an heiress is no felony,
  Whatever to do it with me as the seizer may be.'

Another silence sinks. And a cloud comes over the moon:
The print of the panes upon them enfeebles, as fallen in a swoon,
   Until they are left in darkness unbroke and profound,
As likewise are left their chill and chiselled neighbours around.

HE NEVER EXPECTED MUCH
[or]
A CONSIDERATION

[*A reflection*] ON MY EIGHTY-SIXTH BIRTHDAY

WELL, World, you have kept faith with me,
      Kept faith with me;
Upon the whole you have proved to be
      Much as you said you were.
Since as a child I used to lie
Upon the leaze and watch the sky,
Never, I own, expected I
      That life would all be fair.

'Twas then you said, and since have said,
      Times since have said,
In that mysterious voice you shed
      From clouds and hills around:
'Many have loved me desperately,
Many with smooth serenity,
While some have shown contempt of me
      Till they dropped underground.

'I do not promise overmuch,
      Child; overmuch;
Just neutral-tinted haps and such,'
      You said to minds like mine.
Wise warning for your credit's sake!
Which I for one failed not to take,
And hence could stem such strain and ache
      As each year might assign.

'I TRAVEL AS A PHANTOM NOW'

I TRAVEL as a phantom now,
For people do not wish to see
In flesh and blood so bare a bough
      As Nature makes of me.

And thus I visit bodiless
Strange gloomy households often at odds,
And wonder if Man's consciousness
      Was a mistake of God's.

And next I meet you, and I pause,
And think that if mistake it were,
As some have said, O then it was
      One that I well can bear!

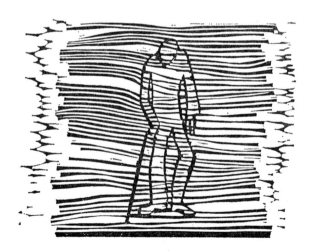

Dear Member

Because we like our Prospectus to be as
accurate as possible, we made a late
change to the production details of our
June book, <u>English Eccentrics</u> by Edith
Sitwell. In a moment of misguided
enthusiasm the printers made this change
twice, so that the production details of
<u>The Portrait of a Lady</u> by Henry James now
look exactly the same.

May we assure our readers that we have not
shortchanged that great novelist by
cramming him onto 284 pages? This
wonderful book is in fact printed on 528
pages plus 16 plates, and is set in
stately Granjon. The size is Royal 8vo
(10" x 6 1/4"), and the daffodil motif
blocked onto the buckram binding is
repeated with lavish profusion on the
endpapers, as you can see overleaf.

In fact, the production details of <u>The
Portrait of a Lady</u> are - we believe -
entirely appropriate to this cornerstone
of English and American literature, and we
apologise for any confusion.

Jocelyn Stoddard

Jocelyn Stoddard
Marketing Director

AFTERWARDS

WHEN the Present has latched its postern behind my tremulous stay,
    And the May month flaps its glad green leaves like wings,
Delicate-filmed as new-spun silk, will the neighbours say,
    'He was a man who used to notice such things'?

If it be in the dusk when, like an eyelid's soundless blink,
    The dewfall-hawk comes crossing the shades to alight
Upon the wind-warped upland thorn, a gazer may think,
    'To him this must have been a familiar sight.'

If I pass during some nocturnal blackness, mothy and warm,
    When the hedgehog travels furtively over the lawn,
One may say, 'He strove that such innocent creatures should come to no
                                    harm,
    But he could do little for them; and now he is gone.'

If, when hearing that I have been stilled at last, they stand at the door,
    Watching the full-starred heavens that winter sees,
Will this thought rise on those who will meet my face no more,
    'He was one who had an eye for such mysteries'?

And will any say when my bell of quittance is heard in the gloom,
    And a crossing breeze cuts a pause in its outrollings,
Till they rise again, as they were a new bell's boom,
    'He hears it not now, but used to notice such things'?

SURVIEW

'Cogitavi vias meas'

A CRY from the green-grained sticks of the fire
    Made me gaze where it seemed to be:
'Twas my own voice talking therefrom to me
On how I had walked when my sun was higher –
    My heart in its arrogancy.

'*You held not to whatsoever was true,*'
    Said my own voice talking to me:
'*Whatsoever was just you were slack to see;*
Kept not things lovely and pure in view,'
    Said my own voice talking to me.

'*You slighted her that endureth all,*'
    Said my own voice talking to me;
'*Vaunteth not, trusteth hopefully;*
That suffereth long and is kind withal,'
    Said my own voice talking to me.

'*You taught not that which you set about,*'
    Said my own voice talking to me;
'*That the greatest of things is Charity. . . .*'
– And the sticks burnt low, and the fire went out,
    And my voice ceased talking to me.

INDEX TO FIRST LINES